Mummy and Me

This book belongs to:

This edition published by Parragon Books Ltd in 2018

Parragon Books Ltd
Chartist House
15–17 Trim Street
Bath BA1 1HA, UK
www.parragon.com

Written by Tiya Hall
Illustrated by Sydney Hanson
Edited by Lily Holland
Designed by Kathryn Davies

ISBN 978-1-5270-1810-5

Printed in China

Mummy and Me

Parragon

Bath • New York • Cologne • Melbourne • Delhi
Hong Kong • Shenzhen • Singapore

The sky is blue, the sun is bright,
I'm **happy** as can be.
I'm ready for a day of fun...
Just my **mum** and **me**!

We **paddle** in the river,

We **splash** about and swim,

And if I'm feeling very **brave**...

We do a **big jump** in!

If I can't see what's ahead
Or if I'm feeling **small**,

She lifts me on her shoulder
So that I feel big and **tall**.

We **hide** and **seek** together,

And we **jump** about and play,

We **roll** around and **giggle**,

We love playing games all day.

And if I'm feeling funny,
Or a little bit **unsure**,

We **roll** around and **giggle**,

We love playing games all day.

We spend our days
exploring,

And building
secret dens,

Having new adventures,
And making **lots** of **friends**.

And if I'm feeling funny,
Or a little bit **unsure**,

She finds a way to **help**,
So I'm not worried any more!

It's true I sometimes make **mistakes,**

But mummy doesn't mind.

She shows me how
to try again,

She's patient
and she's kind.

My mummy loves to **twirl** and **dance**,
We love to whirl and spin.

She knows the **words** to every song...

And I love **joining** in.

I tell her all my **secrets**,
She never breathes a word.

And then she tells me all her **jokes**,
The silliest I've heard!

If I'm feeling **scared** or lonely,
Or if I'm feeling sad,

My mummy always **listens**
So that I don't feel so bad.

At night we count up all the stars,
And look out into space.
Warm and safe in mummy's arms
Is such a special place.

Snuggled up with mummy
Is as cosy as can be.
I really love my mummy,
And I know that she loves me!